Mindful Millie

Louise Tribble

Illustrated by Rhiannon Thomas

*Dedicated to positive mental health
and a positive future for the next generation.*

Mindful Millie

Written by Louise Tribble
Illustrated by Rhiannon Thomas

Today, Millie is going for a walk.

What do you think she can feel, see, hear, and smell?

Millie found a leaf on the floor, she is looking at it mindfully.

"It is green with bits of brown, its stalk is thin and there are lots of little lines," thought Millie.

Can you find an object and look at it mindfully?

What does it feel like?
Does it smell?
Does it make a noise?
Is it warm or cold?

Try eating mindfully.

Place the food to your lips and notice how it feels. Does it smell?

Place the food in your mouth, how does it feel? How does it taste?

"I feel sad today," said Ellie.

Millie knows that when her friends are sad she needs to be mindful of how she talks to them.

"Oh Ellie, I am sorry you are sad," said Millie.

After going home, Millie sends a letter to Ellie.

Write a letter to your friend to let them know you care about them.

"Thank you, Millie. I did what you said in your letter and I feel much better!" said Ellie.

The End

Louise Tribble

I have struggled with mental illness since childhood. I graduated from university in 2015 with a degree in Education and Early Childhood studies. Here I began to appreciate the importance of early intervention in mental health. After years of struggling I learnt mindfulness and have found a new lease of life. My main passion now is promoting positive mental health. I wrote this book to help young children develop skills to create positive mental health as they grow, thus enabling them to cope with whatever life may bring. Mindfulness is all about being in the present - not the past and not the future -but right now.

https://mindfulmillieweb.wordpress.com/

Rhiannon Thomas

The reason behind my style: For me, that fluid style of painting that I adopt with its random application and haphazard splodges, are all geared towards appealing to children. More than anything else, I want those looking at it to realise that you don't have to be perfect to be beautiful. It's about going against the grain and what is expected of you. We're so often taught that to paint 'properly' we have to stay 'inside the lines'. I'm challenging that concept and proving to children that what society dictates as 'normal' isn't necessarily perfect. It's good to experiment and stay adventurous with art and who's to say that's wrong? For me my illustrations are a message to let children break away from the usual constraints. It's very difficult to contain creativity to a set structure - especially when children are involved - and so the best practice is to give them a real sense of freedom and let them run with it.

http://www.moogledoo.com/

Millie the elephant lives life in the present. She uses mindfulness to capture every moment and to help others by teaching them techniques to build a positive mental health. Join Millie with your children and we can build a positive future together.

Printed in Great
Britain
by Amazon